D1287356

WHEN I GO TO THE MOON

DEDICATED
TO MY
MOTHER

When I go
to the
MOON

By Claudia Lewis

Illustrated by Leonard Weisgard

Text © Claudia Lewis 1961
Illustrations © Leonard Weisgard 1961
Library of Congress catalog card number: 60-16850
First Printing
The Macmillan Company, New York
Brett-Macmillan Ltd., Galt, Ontario
Printed in the United States of America

THE MACMILLAN COMPANY

NEW YORK   1961

When I go to the moon
I'll let the scientists explore the craters.

4519

What I want to see is the earth.
I want to look back—
No, not back, but up—
At that great lighted ball,
This world,
That will float there among the old stars
Like a newly created moon.

Imagine the size of it!
Four times larger than the moon we know
And eighty times more bright,
Lighting the moonscape
With white earthlight,
A giant globe up in the sky,
Slowly turning as a globe turns,
With North and South America
And Africa
There before my eye.
Why, the whole thing will seem like a mistake!

Imagine the colors!
I'll see them if I look through telescopes
and filters—
Deserts dusty red,
Green fields
And dark green patches that are forest trees,
The North Pole white with ice
And flash! the sunlight
Striking on the seas.
The earth will look like a giant unimaginable
Christmas tree ornament!

Actually,
There's only one sea
Up on that globe—
All the oceans are one,
None bounded
By any dyke or wall,
All, the homes of fish leaping and splashing,
Fish that could easily swim from one to the other.
"Earth" they call it—
Why not "Ocean"?
It's clear to me
There's not as much land up there
As sea.

I'll sit on a moon mountain
And look at the shores of Maine
And the Oregon shores.
I'll know that children are there, wading
And playing on the long sandy beaches,
Each child thinking he has come to the edge
of the earth.

I'll wonder how it can be that there are people
in Maine
Who have never seen the people of Oregon—
Only inches to travel!
And can it be that some Australians
Stay on their little island all of their lives?

I'll watch the world turning,
Watch the night fall,
Part of the earth still burning bright
While my continent up there
Moves slowly around
To the dark side
Away from the sun's light.

I'll know that a million eyes are turned to look,
then, at the moon where I am,
Old moon in the earth's skies, queen of the heavens—

I'll know the eyes are watching—
Back and forth we'll stare across the cosmic miles,
The electric seas of space
Where rockets are in flight—

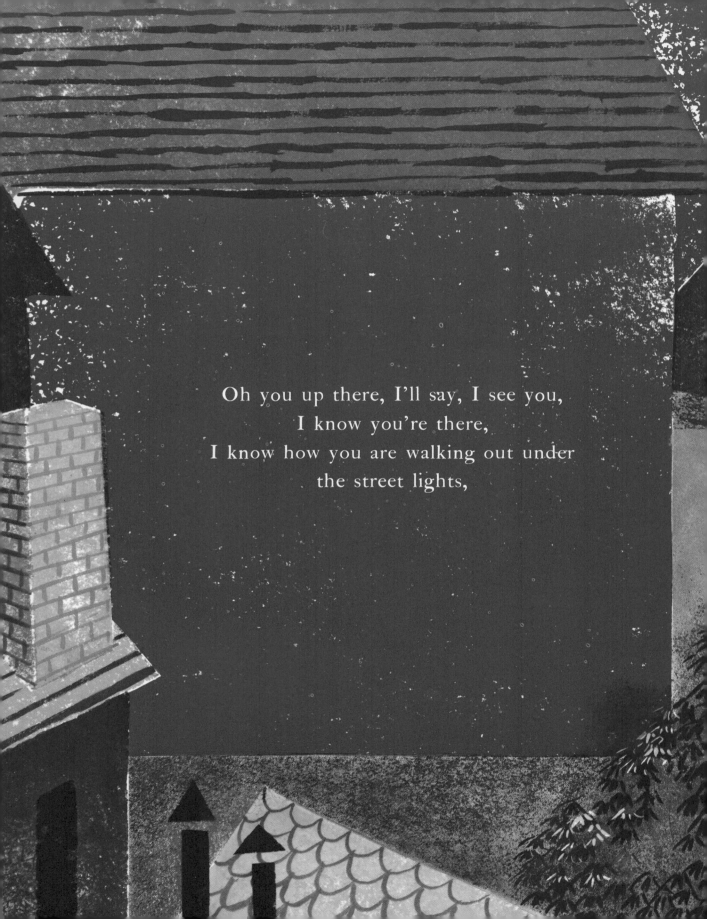

Oh you up there, I'll say, I see you,
I know you're there,
I know how you are walking out under
the street lights,

I know the children are lying in
their beds watching the moon through the windows—
Do you know I am thinking of you?

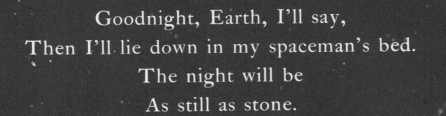

Goodnight, Earth, I'll say,
Then I'll lie down in my spaceman's bed.
The night will be
As still as stone.

But I'll know that while I sleep
The moon is circling round
And gently pulling at earth's seas.
The tides are moving
On the shores at home.

The earth is near.
Goodnight, I'll say,
All's well here,
Is all well there?